Sheltie in Danger

Peter Clover

PUFFIN BOOKS

PUFFIN BOOKS

Published by the Penguin Group
Penguin Books Ltd, 80 Strand, London WC2R 0RL, England
Penguin Putnam Inc., 375 Hudson Street, New York, New York 10014, USA
Penguin Books Australia Ltd, 250 Camberwell Road, Camberwell, Victoria 3124, Australia
Penguin Books Canada Ltd, 10 Alcorn Avenue, Toronto, Ontario, Canada M4V 3B2
Penguin Books India (P) Ltd, 11 Community Centre, Panchsheel Park, New Delhi – 110 017, India
Penguin Books (NZ) Ltd, Cnr Rosedale and Airborne Roads, Albany, Auckland, New Zealand
Penguin Books (South Africa) (Pty) Ltd, 24 Sturdee Avenue, Rosebank 2196, South Africa

Penguin Books Ltd, Registered Offices: 80 Strand, London WC2R 0RL, England

www.penguin.com

Sheltie in Danger first published in Puffin Books 1997
Sheltie to the Rescue first published in Puffin Books 1997
This edition published 2002
10

Copyright © Working Partners Ltd, 1997
All rights reserved

Created by Working Partners Ltd, London W6 0HE

The moral right of the author/illustrator has been asserted

Filmset in 14/22 Palatino

Made and printed in England by Clays Ltd, St Ives plc

Except in the United States of America, this book is sold subject to the condition that it shall not, by way
of trade or otherwise, be lent, re-sold, hired out, or otherwise circulated without the publisher's prior
consent in any form of binding or cover other than that in which it is published and without a similar
condition including this condition being imposed on the subsequent purchaser

British Library Cataloguing in Publication Data
A CIP catalogue record for this book is available from the British Library

ISBN 0–141–31389–7

Contents

Sheltie in Danger

To Vicki and Mark

Chapter One

It was Saturday, and a cold and
wintry morning in Little Applewood.
Emma leaped out of bed and pulled
on her dressing gown. She went over
to the bedroom window and looked
out on to the meadows and rolling
hills of the countryside. Everything
was crisp and white with the early
morning frost.

Sheltie, Emma's Shetland pony,

stood by the fence in his paddock at the bottom of the garden. He stood there every morning, patiently waiting for Emma to appear at the window.

When Sheltie saw her he stamped his hoofs and blew a raspberry. Sheltie's warm breath made little white clouds in the frosty air. To Emma he looked like a big friendly dragon blowing smoke over the top of the wooden fence.

Emma got dressed in her warmest clothes. She put on two woolly jumpers and pulled on her new boots. A long red scarf, which her mum had knitted, hung across the back of a chair. Emma took the scarf and wrapped it around her neck. She felt cosy and warm, wrapped up against the cold.

Downstairs, Dad was laying out the breakfast things on the kitchen table. A saucepan of porridge was already bubbling on the stove, and the smell of sizzling bacon filled the cottage.

'Morning, Emma,' said Mum brightly. 'Breakfast in ten minutes.'

'OK, Mum,' Emma replied.

'Morny,' gurgled Joshua. Joshua was Emma's little brother. He was already sitting up at the kitchen table, playing with his spoon.

Outside, the air was crisp and fresh. Emma pulled the scarf up over her nose and went down to the paddock to give Sheltie his breakfast.

Sheltie didn't mind the cold weather at all. He had already grown his thick winter coat and was as warm as toast. Sheltie's mane and tail were so thick that any brush or comb became tangled up in the long straggly hair.

As Emma scooped Sheltie's pony mix into the feed manger, Sheltie grabbed one end of her scarf between his teeth and pulled.

Sheltie wouldn't let go of the scarf and Emma found herself in a game of tug-of-war and ended up with no scarf at all. Emma laughed as Sheltie galloped around the paddock, the scarf flying along behind him like a red banner.

When Sheltie came back he

dropped the scarf on the grass at
Emma's feet. It was wet and soggy at
one end.

'You are cheeky, Sheltie,' said
Emma. But she could never be cross
with him for long. Sheltie was such a
lovable little pony.

7

While Sheltie gobbled up his breakfast Emma put some hay in the rack on the back wall of the field shelter. Then she filled the drinking trough outside with water.

It was a lovely winter's day. The sky was clear blue and the sun shone brightly even though it was icy cold. The spiky grass was silver with frost.

Mum called to Emma from the back door and Emma hurried in for her breakfast.

'Bye, Sheltie. I'll see you later.'

Chapter Two

It was warm and cosy in the kitchen.
Emma sat down to a bowl of hot
porridge and a plate of bacon and
buttered toast.

Outside, a little robin landed on
the window sill and tapped on
the glass pane with its beak.
Joshua waved his spoon and the
little robin cocked his head to one
side.

'Can we give the robin some toast?' asked Emma.

'We can do better than that,' said Dad. 'I've been making a bird table so that we can feed all the birds right through the winter. It's nearly finished.'

'We can hang up nuts and put out bird seed and water,' said Mum.

'And bacon rind,' chirped Emma. 'Birds like that too!'

After breakfast Dad disappeared into his tool shed and set to work. He liked to make things in his shed. In no time at all he had finished the bird table. It even had perches and little pegs on which to hang bacon rind and bags of nuts.

They put the bird table down at the end of the garden. Sheltie stood looking over the top rail of the paddock fence, watching the birds feeding.

Sheltie wiggled his nose and showed his pony teeth in a funny grin. He wanted to eat some of the toast and breadcrumbs from the table, but it was too far away for him to reach.

Mum placed a shallow dish of water on the table and they all stood back as the robin came and took a drink.

The bird table could be easily seen through the kitchen window, so they went back inside and watched as all the other birds came to feed.

Emma brought out some paper and
coloured pencils, then sat down at
the kitchen table with Joshua, to
draw the robin and all his friends.

Later that morning, Sally came over
on Minnow, her pony. Sally was
Emma's best friend and they often
went riding together. The two girls

decided to ride over to Horseshoe
Pond and gather pine cones in the
wood behind Mr Brown's meadow.

Emma's mum was making table
decorations for the village craft shop
and had asked Emma to bring home
as many pine cones as she could find.

'The woods will be full of them,'
said Emma.

Sheltie and Minnow walked side
by side along the lane. Minnow was
bigger than Sheltie. Sheltie's head
only came up to Minnow's neck, but
he had strong little legs and could
trot just as fast as Minnow.

Sheltie liked Minnow and kept
nuzzling up to him with his nose as
they walked along.

The water in Horseshoe Pond was

like a mirror, still and silver with a thin covering of ice. The pond was in the shape of a giant horseshoe and, where its two ends almost met, there was a little hump of grass like an island.

A duck was sitting on the island, watching some others swimming about in a patch of water which hadn't yet quite frozen over.

'If it gets any colder the ducks won't have any water left to swim in at all,' said Emma.

'And if the ice gets really thick, we'll be able to go ice-skating,' said Sally.

Emma was thrilled at the idea of skating on Horseshoe Pond. She could hardly wait!

The two girls stood watching
the ducks for a while, then walked
the ponies up towards the
woods.

All the leaves had fallen from the
trees and there were pine cones
scattered everywhere. Emma and
Sally tied Sheltie and Minnow loosely
to a bare branch and left them
munching grass while they began
gathering up the cones.

In no time at all they had filled two
plastic carrier bags.

'Mum will be able to make heaps
of decorations with all these!' said
Emma.

Sheltie had found an enormous
cone beneath the tree and picked it
up carefully in his mouth. Emma

carried it home and let Sheltie
present it to Mum himself.

'What a clever pony you are,
Sheltie,' said Mum. 'It's the biggest
pine cone I've ever seen!'

Chapter Three

The very next day it snowed. When Emma woke, her bedroom window was white with frost. She pressed her nose against the cold glass pane and peered outside. Snowflakes the size of ten-pence pieces drifted lazily down from the sky and lay gently on the ground.

Outside, everything was covered with a thick blanket of snow. The garden path had disappeared completely and Sheltie's paddock had turned from green to a glistening white. The distant hills had changed into white mountains of snow.

Sheltie stood at the fence, up to his knees in a drift of white, powdery snow. His long shaggy mane was frosted white, and beneath his fringe his eyes sparkled like diamonds.

Emma dressed quickly and hurried downstairs to look for her boots. They were where she had left them, by the kitchen door.

Feeding Sheltie that morning was more fun than usual. The snowfall had made Sheltie friskier than ever and he was in a playful mood.

Each time Emma bent over, Sheltie

18

nudged her with his muzzle and sent
Emma headlong into the snow.

Emma made snowballs and chased
Sheltie around the paddock. Sheltie
thought this was great fun and tried

to eat all the snowballs that Emma
threw at him.

Mum and Dad came out of the
cottage with Joshua, to watch the
snowball fight. They stood by the
fence as Sheltie galloped round and
round the paddock, chasing the
snowballs and falling snowflakes.

'I'll make you a sleigh,' said Dad.
'If this snow keeps up, Sheltie will be
able to pull it along and give you
some lovely rides.'

Sheltie seemed to like this idea and he swished his tail to and fro. He shook the snow from his mane and blew a white cloud of steam from his nostrils.

Chapter Four

The snow fell for most of Sunday. By late afternoon Little Applewood was completely covered in a crisp white blanket.

Everything shone white as far as you could see. All the trees glistened with fresh white flakes. The cottage rooftops were thick with snow and their chimney pots wore tall white hats.

Sheltie left deep tracks in the snow wherever he went. Emma put down some more straw on the floor of Sheltie's field shelter to keep his feet dry.

By half-past four it was getting dark and Emma was helping Mum to make the tea. Dad sat at the kitchen table with a pencil and paper, working out how to turn the old toboggan he had found in his shed into a sleigh for Sheltie to pull.

Emma was looking forward to riding on the sleigh and so was Joshua. Being pulled along by Sheltie would be such great fun.

The next morning was the start of Emma's half-term holiday from school. Dad had taken the week off from work too, to do some odd jobs around the cottage and to look after Emma and Joshua whenever Mum was busy at the village craft shop.

Dad had disappeared into his shed to start work on the sleigh. It was going to be a surprise, so Emma wasn't allowed to peep until it was finished.

As Emma fed Sheltie his breakfast she could hear banging and sawing coming from inside the shed. Dad was fixing two shafts on to the toboggan. She told Sheltie that he was going to have a sleigh to pull, and he seemed very excited.

Mum and Joshua put some breadcrumbs out on the bird table,

then went into the paddock to help Emma and Sheltie make a snowman.

First Emma made a big snowball. Then she rolled it around the paddock until it grew bigger and bigger. When it was big enough to be the snowman's body Emma rolled it across to the gate. Sheltie helped and gave it a push with his nose.

Then they made a smaller snowball for the snowman's head. Mum put the head on top of the body and pushed a carrot into the snowball to make a long nose. Sheltie was very naughty and tried to pull the carrot out. Sheltie liked carrots and wanted to eat it, so Emma had to go and fetch him another one as a treat.

They made eyes for the snowman

with two small lumps of coal and a
smiley mouth from little stones. Then
Emma wrapped her scarf around its
neck and Mum popped a woolly hat
on top of the snowman's head. It
made him look quite grand.

Sheltie cocked his head to one side and looked at the snowman. Then he pawed at the snow with his hoof and wanted to play. But the snowman didn't move. He wasn't as much fun as Emma, so Sheltie gave him a hard nudge and knocked his head off. Then he grabbed the carrot nose and galloped off with it across the paddock.

Chapter Five

Later that morning, Sally came over
on Minnow and the two girls rode
over to Mr Brown's meadow to see if
Horseshoe Pond had frozen over
completely.

It had! When they got there,
Mr Brown was standing in the
middle of the thick ice, where
the pond curved. He saw the two
girls on their ponies and jumped up

and down on the ice to test its strength.

'I expect you two will be up here with your skates now!' said Mr Brown. 'It's rock solid.' He gave a friendly wave, then slipped and sat down on the ice with a bump.

Emma and Sally started to laugh. Mr Brown was laughing too and Sheltie gave a funny snort.

'I think I'll leave the skating to you youngsters,' he said as he pulled himself to his feet.

Emma and Sally jumped down from their saddles and landed almost up to their knees in a drift of soft snow. They left Sheltie and Minnow under the sycamore tree. A patch of green grass was still showing through the white snow where the ground was sheltered beneath the tree branches.

Sheltie and Minnow lowered their heads and munched at the grass.

Emma stepped carefully out on to the ice. It was very slippery and difficult to walk on at first. Sally took a run at it and did a big slide across the surface of the pond.

'This is brilliant!' said Sally. 'I can't wait to get my ice-skates on.'

Emma didn't have any ice-skates, but Sally had a spare pair at home. She said that she would teach Emma to skate, so the two friends trotted on their ponies all the way to Fox Hall Manor and back to fetch them.

When they returned, Horseshoe Pond shone and glistened like

polished glass. Emma and Sally sat
on the snowy bank and put on their
skates. Sheltie and Minnow stood by
watching. Sheltie was very interested
in what was going on.

When Sally stood up on the ice and
went gliding across the pond, Sheltie's
ears pricked up in surprise and he
made a funny snorting noise.

Although Emma had never been
ice-skating before, she was very good
on roller skates. The slippery ice felt
odd beneath her feet and she was a
bit wobbly at first.

Sally held Emma's hand and led
her on to the ice and around the
pond. When Sheltie saw Emma
skating, he trotted over to the edge of
the pond and put one hoof on the ice.

'No, Sheltie,' said Emma. 'You can't skate. Stay there and watch.'

But Sheltie didn't want to stay and watch. He wanted to skate across the ice like Emma.

Emma hoped that Sheltie was going to behave. She knew he was very determined. Minnow was a very quiet pony, but he did tend to copy everything that Sheltie did, and the last thing that Emma wanted was two ponies skidding on the ice.

Sheltie calmed down and stepped back from the pond. He watched Emma skating, from beneath the tree.

Emma learned very quickly and was soon skating on her own, round and round Horseshoe Pond. Then she slipped and fell down on the ice with her legs waving in the air.

Sally laughed and went to help Emma back up on to her feet. But the ice was so slippery and the two girls were laughing so much that they

both ended up in a heap, sprawled
across the icy surface of the pond.

Sheltie thought that this looked
like great fun and wanted to join in.
He dashed down on to the ice and
slid on all fours right across the pond
to the other side.

Sheltie went so fast that when he reached the far bank he gave a little hop and landed back on the grass.

'Look at Sheltie,' laughed Sally. 'He can skate!'

'The world's first skating pony,' said Emma.

Sheltie looked more surprised than anyone. He glanced back across the ice with a puzzled look as if to say, 'How did I do that?'

Sheltie kept away from the ice from then on. He was happy to stand with Minnow and watch.

The two girls continued skating until it was time to go home for their lunch.

Chapter Six

Dad was sitting in the kitchen having a mug of hot tea and looking very pleased with himself. He told Emma that Sheltie's sleigh was almost finished.

'Let's hope the snow doesn't melt overnight,' said Dad, 'then you and Sheltie can have some real fun tomorrow.'

Emma helped Mum to clear away

the plates after lunch and wash and
dry the dishes. Then she decided to
ride Sheltie back over to Horseshoe
Pond. Emma wanted to practise her
skating again so that she would be as
good as Sally.

Sheltie stood by the edge of the
pond and watched as Emma sat on
the snowy bank and put on Sally's
spare ice-skates.

Emma was a lot better already and
didn't wobble half as much as before.
Each time she skated round the pond
and passed Sheltie she gave him a
little wave.

And each time Emma went by
Sheltie tossed his head and gave a
little snort.

Then a terrible thing happened.

The ice wasn't as thick as Emma had thought. Around the edge of the pond the ice was as solid as a rock. But further in, where the water was deeper, there was a patch of ice that was thinner than the rest. Even Mr Brown hadn't seen it.

The first time Emma had skated across that spot, the ice had cracked a little but not enough for Emma to notice. But the second time, the ice gave way completely and Emma fell right through into the freezing water beneath.

Emma let out a scream as she fell. Although the water only came up to just past her waist, it was icy cold. Her feet got stuck in the muddy goo on the pond bed and the cold water took her breath away.

'Help, Sheltie! Help!' cried Emma.

Sheltie was quick to act. The moment he saw Emma disappear through the hole in the ice he raced to her rescue.

Sheltie's hoofs slipped and skidded on the ice as he dashed forward on to the pond.

Although Sheltie was only a small pony, he was very heavy, and his weight made the thin ice around the hole crack and give way.

As Sheltie reached Emma, the ice broke away completely beneath him and he plunged down into the water beside her.

Emma grabbed Sheltie's mane and

managed to scramble up on to the
ice. Emma was soaked right through,
but she was safely out of the freezing
water and stood on the solid ice
away from the hole.

But Sheltie's feet were stuck. He

couldn't move and was standing up to his neck in the icy water. He struggled to climb back up on to the frozen surface, but he couldn't. Poor Sheltie remained trapped as he whinnied and blew with loud snorts. The more he struggled, the more stuck he became.

'Hang on, Sheltie!' cried Emma. She was shaking with fright. 'I'll go for help.'

Emma pulled off the skates and ran as fast as she could back to the cottage.

Chapter Seven

Emma was sobbing as she ran. By the time she burst through the back door into the kitchen her eyes were red and puffy.

Her clothes were soaked right through and her legs were covered with slimy mud. She was shaking and crying as she fell into Mum's arms.

'Emma!' cried Mum. 'What on earth has happened?' She put her

arms around Emma and pushed the
wet hair away from her eyes.

Emma was so upset she could
hardly speak. 'It's . . . it's . . . Sheltie.
He's fallen into the pond . . . We've got
to help him. The ice broke and I fell in.
Sheltie saved me but now he's stuck.
Oh, Mum! It's freezing. Poor Sheltie
will freeze to death. We've got to get
him out! We've got to help him!'

Emma managed to blurt out the
story in one breath, then she hugged
Mum tightly. She couldn't stop
herself from shaking.

Dad flew down the stairs. He had
heard what had happened and
rushed out into the hall to get his
coat.

'I'll fetch the car,' said Dad. 'There

are ropes in the boot.' He told Mum to telephone Mr Brown and ask him to come to the pond with his tractor. Then he ran outside to the car and sped off up the lane.

Mum made the phone call to Mr Brown, then got Emma out of her wet clothes and ran a hot bath.

Emma sat by the kitchen range wrapped in a thick blanket, warming herself by the open fire. She was so worried. All she could think of was poor Sheltie stuck in the freezing cold pond.

Dad drove the car right through the double gates and across the meadow to Horseshoe Pond. The car tyres left dark tracks in the white snow.

As Dad jumped out of the car he saw Sheltie's head sticking out above the ice in the middle of the pond.

'It's all right, Sheltie!' he called out. 'Hang on, boy. We'll soon get you out of there!'

Sheltie let out a feeble snort. He was freezing cold and feeling very weak. Struggling to get out of the pond had made his feet well and truly stuck in the gooey mud. Sheltie was tired and very frightened.

Dad took a rope from the car and made a loop at one end. But he couldn't see how he could tie the rope to Sheltie to pull him out.

It was hopeless. And poor Sheltie was unable to climb up out of the hole on his own.

Across the snowy meadow came
Mr Brown, chugging along in his
tractor. He had several long planks of
wood in the back and laid them across
the ice to stand on. Then Mr Brown

took a sledgehammer and began smashing the ice. He made a rough little path from the hole to the near edge of the pond.

'I've called the fire brigade,' said Mr Brown. 'They should be here any minute.'

Suddenly a blue flashing light appeared. Emma's dad called out and waved the fire engine over to the pond.

Carefully, the firemen reversed the engine right up to the edge of the snowy bank. A strong ladder swung out over the pond, and Emma's dad watched as they passed a cable through the rungs and attached it to a winch.

One fireman had jumped into the

freezing water and was talking
quietly to Sheltie.

'Don't worry, boy. We'll soon have
you out,' he said.

Sheltie answered with a weak
whinny.

The fireman fitted a sling around Sheltie's tummy, then hooked the sling to the cable overhead. He stayed with Sheltie as the winch droned and began to turn.

There was a squelching noise as Sheltie's hoofs came free of the muddy goo and weeds. Then, slowly, the little pony was lifted clear of the icy water and gently lowered on to the bank.

Sheltie was puffing and blowing with fright, but at last he was standing safely on dry land.

Chapter Eight

Poor Sheltie was covered in sticky mud. His coat and mane were plastered to his body with icy water. Emma's little pony was shivering with fright, but he was safe.

Mr Brown took some blankets from the tractor and threw them over Sheltie.

'Best try to get most of the water out and dry him off,' said Mr Brown.

Dad rubbed Sheltie's face and mane with a blanket while Mr Brown set to work on Sheltie's back. Then both men started drying his sides and legs. Sheltie's tail was sopping wet. The blankets were soaked, and the little pony was still dripping.

'Poor thing must be frozen through to his bones,' said Dad.

'You should get him home as quickly as you can,' said Mr Brown. 'Get him moving so that he warms up a bit. And put another dry blanket on him before you walk him back.'

Sheltie's nose was ice cold.

'Poor Sheltie,' said Dad. He stroked Sheltie's head, then replaced the wet blanket with a dry one and led the

51

little pony off across the white
meadow and up the lane.

'I'll come back for the car later,'
Dad called over his shoulder to the
farmer.

Sheltie's legs were wobbly, but he
kept walking until they arrived at the
paddock. Dad put Sheltie into his
field shelter, then raced to the cottage
to fetch more dry blankets and some
old towels.

Emma had dried out now and
wanted to help. When she saw
Sheltie she threw her arms around
his neck and gave him a big hug.

Sheltie sneezed, then closed his
eyes and lowered his head.

'Come on, Emma,' said Dad. 'Let's
get him nice and dry.'

Mum and Joshua came out to the
stable with two mugs of hot tea.
Mum helped to dry Sheltie off with
one of the towels.

Sheltie's thick woolly coat was

getting drier by the minute, but he was still cold and shivering. Dad put lots of straw down on the floor and threw a nice dry blanket over him. Then he packed some more straw underneath Sheltie's blanket for extra warmth.

'We can't do any more,' said Dad. 'Let's hope Sheltie dries out quickly on his own.' He went inside to telephone Mr Thorne, the vet, and asked him to come over to take a look at Sheltie.

When the vet arrived it was already pitch dark. The sky looked as though it was full of snow again and the temperature had dropped to freezing.

Sheltie looked sad and miserable.

'He's had quite a scare,' said Mr Thorne. 'And the poor thing is frozen right through. We can only hope that he warms up and doesn't get ill.'

The vet gave Sheltie an injection and said that they should keep a close eye on him. He would pop over in the morning to see how Sheltie was feeling.

'He's a tough little Shetland,' Mr Thorne said. 'He's used to the cold weather. But you must keep him warm and hope for the best.'

Mum stroked Emma's hair.

'Don't worry, Emma,' she said. 'We'll look after Sheltie. He'll be all right.'

Chapter Nine

Emma didn't sleep a wink all night. She kept thinking about poor Sheltie. She couldn't bear the thought of him being unwell. If anything should happen to him . . .

Emma sobbed into her pillow.

The next morning, Emma got dressed quicker than ever, and ran down to the paddock.

It had been snowing in the night and the snow was even thicker. All the tracks and footprints from the previous day had disappeared. Emma raced across the paddock to the field shelter.

Sheltie looked awful. He wasn't perky at all. He just stood there, staring straight ahead, hardly moving.

Emma whispered Sheltie's name and stroked his neck. He was sweating slightly and his coat felt damp. He gave a sneeze and Emma saw that his nose was runny and his eyes were watery.

Emma pulled some hay from the rack and offered it in her hand. Slowly, Sheltie took the feed and

tried to eat, but after a moment the
hay just fell to the floor.

Emma put a scoop of pony mix
into the manger, but poor Sheltie
wasn't interested. He gave another
sneeze and started to cough.

Emma ran back to the cottage to
fetch Mum.

*

Mr Thorne, the vet, came back just after breakfast. He examined Sheltie and took the little pony's temperature.

'I'm afraid Sheltie has a fever.' Mr Thorne looked worried. 'As I suspected yesterday, he's caught a bad cold.'

'Is there anything we can do?' asked Mum.

'We can only hope it doesn't develop into something much worse,' said the vet.

Emma looked up at Mum.

'Sheltie will be all right, won't he?'

'We'll do whatever we can,' said Mum. 'We'll look after him. We'll do our best. We all will.'

Dad and Joshua nodded.

The vet gave Sheltie another injection and said that all they could do was to keep him warm and quiet.

Sheltie was a very poorly little pony.

Sheltie's field shelter was closed in on three sides but one wall was open and looked out across the paddock.

Mr Thorne said that they should pile bales of straw across the wide opening to keep out the cold wind. And he gave Mum a small bottle of brown liquid and said that they should add a few drops to a bowl of hot water so that Sheltie could breathe in the fumes. It would help Sheltie's cough and make it easier for him to breathe.

'Make up a bran mash to keep up

his strength,' added Mr Thorne. 'Try to get him to eat. Spoon-feed him if you have to. And bathe his eyes with warm water.'

Emma swallowed hard. She was very upset.

Dad spoke quietly. 'Is there a good chance of Sheltie getting better?' he asked.

'We can only hope for the best,' said the vet. 'Sheltie is going to need lots of love and care.'

Emma stood up straight. Sheltie had saved her life. She was determined to nurse him back to health.

Chapter Ten

'Right,' said Dad. 'Let's get those bales of straw. I'll drive over to the farm straight away.'

While Dad went to fetch the bales, Emma laid down a thick bedding of straw all around Sheltie and packed fresh, dry straw underneath his blanket.

Poor Sheltie stood with his head held low. His ears, normally alert and pointy, lay floppy against his head and he looked very sick. Then he let out a loud sneeze and began to cough.

Dad came back with twelve bales of straw and Emma helped to pile them across the open end of the shelter. It was much warmer inside now.

Mum appeared, with Joshua trailing behind her. 'Here's that bowl of hot water,' she said.

The drops of liquid in the hot water gave off a lovely smelling vapour. Emma took a deep breath. It was like strong peppermint.

Emma held the bowl near Sheltie and the steam drifted up towards him. Sheltie's nostrils twitched at

the peppermint smell and it seemed
to help him to breathe more easily.
The vet had also said that they

should bathe Sheltie's eyes, so Mum took some cotton wool and another bowl of warm water. Emma watched as Mum carefully wiped his eyes and lashes.

Dad changed the blanket for a nice dry one that had been warming on the kitchen range. They made Sheltie as comfortable as they could.

'Poor, poor Sheltie,' whispered Emma as she gently stroked the little pony's mane. She felt really sad seeing Sheltie like this and felt a pain like a knot in her tummy.

In the afternoon, Sally came riding over on Minnow. When she saw Emma's face she knew immediately that something was wrong. Sally hadn't heard about the accident.

'What is it, Emma?' she asked.

Emma swallowed hard, gulping back her tears. She really was trying to be brave.

'It's Sheltie,' she said. 'I fell through the ice on Horseshoe Pond and Sheltie saved me. But now he's very ill.' The words seemed to stick in Emma's throat.

Sally could tell by Emma's voice that it was serious.

'Is Sheltie going to be all right?' she asked.

Emma's face crumpled. 'I hope so, Sally,' she said.

Sally put her arm around Emma and listened to everything that had happened.

'Oh, poor Sheltie,' said Sally. 'Can I do anything to help?'

Emma shook her head. She had never felt this sad before.

Chapter Eleven

That same afternoon, Dad brought
out his spare car battery and a special
attachment to put up a light in
Sheltie's field shelter. He fitted a
heating bulb into the light socket, to
give Sheltie some extra warmth.

Emma and Mum made a bran
mash just like Mr Thorne had said
and spoon-fed Sheltie with the
mixture.

Sheltie was normally so lively and loved his food, but now he didn't seem to want to eat at all. Emma offered him fresh water in a plastic bucket, but Sheltie just stared at it with his head low.

'He looks worse than ever,' said Emma.

The next day was just as bad. Emma didn't like leaving Sheltie out in the shelter all on his own overnight, but there was nothing else they could do.

The snow had settled and it was very cold. Sweeping white drifts had blown up outside against the stable walls and the air inside was cold and damp.

The heater light was left on all the

time and Emma refreshed the
steaming bowl of peppermint vapour
every hour. It all helped, but Sheltie
was still very poorly.

Emma spent every minute of the
long day with Sheltie. She took
books into the stable and read aloud
to the little pony so that he could
hear her voice and know that she
was there.

Emma told Sheltie how the little
robin had come for his breakfast at
the bird table. And she told the little
pony all about the wonderful sleigh
that Dad had made for him.

'It's even got your name painted
on the side,' said Emma.

Sheltie listened to everything that
Emma said and breathed in the

vapour from the bowl that Emma
had placed at his feet.

Sally came to visit again. She stood
outside the field shelter clutching a
plastic bag.

'I couldn't think of anything else to

bring you,' said Sally, pulling out a
pony magazine and some comics. 'I
brought these as well.' Sally handed
Emma a packet of peppermints.
'They're for Sheltie when he gets
better.'

Sally stayed for lunch. But no one
really felt like eating anything.
Everyone was very upset and waiting
for Mr Thorne's next visit.

When the vet arrived, they all went down to the paddock. There was a terrible shock waiting for them when they stepped into the shelter. Sheltie was lying down on his side on the straw. He was making funny noises and his ribs heaved each time he took a breath.

Sheltie wasn't getting better. In fact, he looked much worse.

Chapter Twelve

The vet was very worried. He put his bag down and examined the little pony.

'I'm afraid Sheltie has taken a turn for the worse,' he said. 'There's nothing more that we can do.'

Sheltie turned his head slightly and opened his eyes to look up at Emma. He whinnied softly, then closed his eyes again.

'Sheltie, Sheltie,' sobbed Emma. She threw herself on to the straw and put her arms around Sheltie's neck.

'You've done everything you can, Emma,' said Mr Thorne. 'It's up to Sheltie now. I'm very sorry.'

Dad took Emma indoors. She and Sally were so upset. Emma's mum took Sally home in the car.

That evening, nobody felt like eating a big meal, so Mum just made some sandwiches and they all sat at the kitchen table.

At bedtime, Mum tucked up Emma with an extra blanket and sat with her until she fell asleep.

But Emma didn't stay asleep for

long. Her thoughts were filled with dreams of poor Sheltie.

When Mum and Dad had gone to bed, Emma got up. She put on her warmest clothes and an extra woolly jumper. She wrapped the spare blanket around her shoulders. Then she tiptoed downstairs to the kitchen and filled a fresh bowl with hot water.

Emma opened the back door quietly and crunched through the snow down to the paddock to visit Sheltie.

The little pony was still lying down, but he looked peaceful, as though he were sleeping soundly.

Emma knelt down and stroked Sheltie's neck. His coat didn't feel

damp with sweat any more. It felt
quite dry, and his ears twitched as
she spoke softly to him.

'You've got to pull through, Sheltie.
You've got to.'

Sheltie gave a little sigh and
opened his eyes.

Emma put the peppermint-
smelling drops into the bowl of hot
water. Then she thought she would
try Sheltie with a little food. She took
a spoon and managed to feed him
some bran mash, a little at a time.
Sheltie seemed to know that he had
to eat in order to get better.

'Good boy. Good Sheltie,' said
Emma.

Each time Sheltie took a mouthful,
Emma felt a little more hope. But the

small, sick pony lying on the bed of
straw was not like the Sheltie she
knew. It was hard to imagine him
racing around the paddock, looking
for mischief.

Emma placed the bowl of hot water by Sheltie's head so that he could breathe in the vapour through the rest of the night. She covered him with her blanket and snuggled up against the little Shetland pony.

She lay her head against his neck for a little while before she crept over to the far corner of the shelter and fell asleep, curled up on the soft straw.

Chapter Thirteen

When Emma woke the next morning, at first she didn't know where she was. The sun was rising slowly over the back meadow and the field shelter was filled with a soft golden light.

Emma blinked the sleep from her eyes. She heard a soft whicker. Sheltie!

Emma sat up quickly. She could hardly believe what she saw.

The little Shetland pony was standing up on his feet. He seemed a little unsteady, but he was standing all the same. His eyes looked brighter and he greeted her with a little snort.

As Emma jumped up, Sheltie gave a tiny sneeze. Then he swished his tail and made the funny noises he always did when he was hungry and waiting for his breakfast.

Sheltie was really happy to see Emma. And Emma had never felt so happy in her life. She was so happy she wrapped her arms around Sheltie's neck and gave him a big, long hug.

Emma ran outside. Everything as far as she could see was still covered white with snow. The countryside was quiet and peaceful. All the usual sounds seemed to be muffled by the thick blanket of snow.

Emma raced as fast as her legs could carry her. She ran through the snow and across the paddock. She was in such a hurry to tell Mum and Dad, Emma didn't have time to open the gate, so she climbed over it and ran up the garden to the cottage.

When Emma burst into the kitchen, Mum was getting ready for breakfast. She was very surprised to see Emma up so early.

Emma didn't need to say anything. The delighted look on her face said it all. Sheltie was going to be all right!

Over the next few days, Sheltie got stronger and stronger. He began eating on his own again and soon looked like his old self. There was no more coughing, no more sneezing and no more runny eyes.

Mr Thorne came over to check on Sheltie and gave the little Shetland pony a clean bill of health.

'Sheltie's made a remarkable recovery,' said the vet. 'And I'm certain that it has a lot to do with all the loving care and attention that you've been giving him, Emma.'

Emma beamed a big smile. She was so glad that Sheltie was fit and well again.

'No doubt Sheltie will be wanting to race around in the paddock soon,' said Mr Thorne.

'But it's still very snowy,' said Emma. 'Will Sheltie be all right?'

'Of course he will,' said the vet. 'Sheltie is fine now. He's a tough little Shetland pony.'

Sheltie puffed out his chest and blew a raspberry. Just like he always did.

Chapter Fourteen

It was Saturday morning and the sun shone brightly in the frosty, pale-blue sky. Although it was more than a week later, the white snow still gleamed like icing sugar across the paddock.

Sheltie stood pawing at a soft drift. He was blowing and snorting and eager to get going.

Dad had made a special harness to

fit around Sheltie's chest. And the
two long shafts which were fixed to
the sleigh were strapped in place.

Emma sat on the little wooden seat
holding on to the sides. There were
no reins to steer with. Dad was going
to lead from the front.

'Ready, Emma?'

Emma grinned and nodded.

'Come on, Sheltie,' said Dad. 'Race you around the paddock.' And they were off.

Sheltie trotted easily along, pulling the sleigh smoothly behind him. Dad was puffing like an old train. And Emma was giggling and calling for Sheltie to go faster.

Riding in the sleigh was great fun, especially when they turned corners. Then the sleigh would shoot out to the side really fast.

Emma gave a little scream whenever this happened, and Sheltie answered with a loud snort.

In the afternoon, Sally came over to play. Sheltie was showing off in front of Minnow and pulling the sleigh as fast as his little legs would carry him. Emma was leading Sheltie now and pulling Sally in the sleigh, all around the paddock.

Mum and Dad and Joshua were watching through the kitchen window. Emma was racing in front of Sheltie, holding the lead rope and laughing.

Sheltie was trying to grab the packet of peppermints sticking out of Emma's jacket pocket.

When they stopped, Sheltie nudged Emma headlong into a pile of soft snow.

Sally jumped out of the sleigh and joined Emma in a frosty heap. The two girls had a fit of the giggles and showered each other with snow.

Then Sheltie pinched the packet of peppermints from Emma's pocket and ran off, with the empty sleigh zigzagging behind him.

'He's so funny, isn't he?' laughed Sally.

Sheltie was blowing loud raspberries as he ran.

'I'll give him funny when I catch him!' giggled Emma. And she chased Sheltie all over the paddock.

It was good to have her dearest friend back to his old self again.

Sheltie to
the Rescue

To David Honour

Chapter One

'Don't look so grumpy, Emma. It's supposed to be a holiday,' said Mum.

They were all sitting around the kitchen table looking at brochures: Mum, Dad, little Joshua and Emma.

Mum was looking at lovely pictures of pretty seaside holiday cottages. Dad was studying a large road map spread out across the table. And Joshua was trying to turn the pages of the brochure that Mum was holding.

Emma just sat there with her hands folded in her lap, looking grumpy.

'Two whole weeks,' said Emma. 'It won't be much of a holiday if Sheltie can't come. And who will look after him while we're away?'

Dad looked up from the map, with a frown.

'We told you yesterday, Emma. Mrs Linney is going to pop over every day and feed Sheltie. Mrs Linney knows exactly what to do and how to look after him. There's no need to worry.'

'But it won't be the same,' said Emma. 'Sheltie's *my* pony now. I like looking after him. He'll think I've gone away and left him. He'll be miserable, just like me.'

'A fortnight isn't such a long time,' said Mum. She was beginning to look a little cross. 'Two weeks at the seaside, Emma. Just think of it.'

'I don't want to think about it,' said Emma. 'And I don't want to go. If Sheltie can't come with us then I'd rather stay at home, here in Little Applewood.'

Dad raised an eyebrow. He didn't say anything, but Emma could tell he was thinking hard. Mum ignored Emma and carried on flipping through the brochures.

'Look at this one. A tiny cottage right on top of the cliffs, overlooking the sea.'

Emma glanced at the picture of the little white cottage. But she was too busy thinking about poor Sheltie being left behind with no one to play with for fourteen whole days.

The next morning, Emma went into the paddock to give Sheltie his breakfast. She shovelled a scoop of pony mix into Sheltie's feed manger then gave him an extra tiny handful as a treat.

Sheltie stuck his head into the manger and gobbled up the pellets like a hoover. It always made Emma laugh when Sheltie did that. His head disappeared right inside the bin.

When Sheltie had finished, Emma took the hosepipe from the outside wall and filled his drinking trough.

Sheltie liked the water. He always

tried to drink it straight from the hose. Emma aimed the hose at Sheltie and gave him a squirt. Sheltie blew a loud raspberry, then galloped playfully around the paddock.

When Emma looked up she saw Mum and Dad standing by the paddock gate. They were both smiling. Joshua was there too, sitting across the top bar of the wooden fence. He was squirming like a little worm and Mum was holding on to him tightly.

Emma put the hose away and skipped over to the gate. She was ready for her own breakfast now and as they all sat round the kitchen table Mum told Emma some special news.

'Do you remember the holiday cottage we were looking at yesterday, Emma?' said Mum. 'The one on the cliff-top, overlooking the sea?'

Emma nodded and looked down at her shoes. She didn't want to think about going away on holiday and leaving Sheltie.

'Well, Emma,' said Dad, 'the cottage has a paddock at the back just like Sheltie's.'

'But Sheltie won't be in it, will he?' said Emma in a sulky voice. 'Poor Sheltie will be left behind all on his own!'

Dad raised an eyebrow at Mum then looked at Emma and smiled.

'Oh no he won't,' said Dad. 'I telephoned Mrs Linney this morning and she has a friend who is going to lend us a horse trailer. So now Sheltie can come away on holiday too.'

Emma's face lit up with a big smile and she clapped her hands with excitement.

'Do you really mean it, Dad? Yippee! Now it will be a real holiday for all of us.'

Chapter Two

Two days before the holiday, Dad collected the horse trailer. It looked like a little caravan on wheels. There was a big door at the back and a little window high up at the front for Sheltie to look out and see where he was going. The horse trailer was just the right size to take a little Shetland pony like Sheltie.

'It's just like a little house,' said Emma as she peered inside.

When Emma ran to the paddock and told Sheltie that he was coming on holiday, he became quite frisky and galloped around the little field tossing his head. She was certain he was as excited as she was.

The next morning Emma was busy helping Mum and Dad to pack their suitcases with everything they would need for two weeks by the seaside.

Then in the afternoon Emma helped Dad to load Sheltie's bags of pony mix and several bales of hay into the horse trailer. She hung Sheltie's bridle and saddle on the special hooks behind the door, then spread some straw across the floor.

Everything was ready for an early start the following day.

Bright and early on Friday morning Dad tied the suitcases to the roof-rack on top of the car. Emma put Sheltie's head collar on him and led him up the ramp into the horse trailer.

Sheltie gave a soft blow and looked

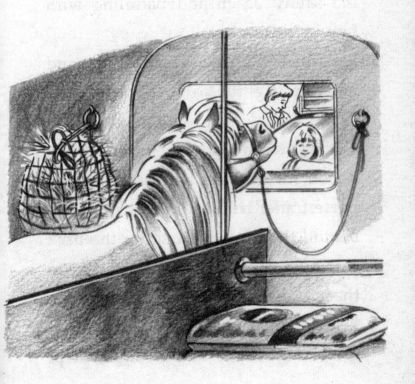

out of the little window. His bright eyes twinkled with excitement beneath his bushy mane.

Sheltie had never been away on holiday before, and Emma was looking forward to galloping along the sandy beach and paddling with him in the sea.

Little Joshua was excited too and held on tightly to his bucket and spade.

It was ten o'clock when they finally set off for Summerland Bay. Sheltie's horse trailer trundled along smoothly behind the car. Emma sat in the back seat next to the window. Mum sat in the back too with Joshua strapped into his special car seat.

As they drove along, Emma kept

looking behind to make sure the horse trailer was still there. Sometimes Emma could see the tip of Sheltie's nose poking through the trailer window. It was open slightly and Sheltie was sniffing the air. She knew he was enjoying every minute of the ride.

The journey took two hours, so it was midday when they finally arrived at their holiday cottage.

Cliff-top Cottage was much smaller than the cottage at Little Applewood. It was whitewashed, with a bright red door. On either side of the door were two little windows. Upstairs there were two bedrooms and a bathroom.

At the back of the cottage was a small paddock for Sheltie. The cottage

itself sat high on the cliff-top, with fields and meadows all around. The rolling heath ran to the edge of the cliff. And below, a footpath wound its way gently down to the sandy beach of Summerland Bay. It was a beautiful spot. The perfect place for a holiday cottage.

Chapter Three

Before they unloaded their suitcases from the roof-rack, Dad helped Emma to settle Sheltie into his paddock.

Sheltie's nostrils twitched as he took in a deep breath of salty air. Sheltie had never smelt the sea before. It made him feel lively and he galloped around his new paddock in a full circle, shaking his long mane and kicking his heels.

Sheltie seemed very happy. And Emma was delighted too.

Dad took the suitcases and carried them into the cottage. Then Emma helped Mum unpack all their things.

Dad made some sandwiches and a pot of tea, and everyone sat down outside at a little table in the garden. Emma and Joshua had fizzy drinks and looked out across the cliff-top at the sparkling sea beyond.

After lunch, they all went for a walk to explore the footpath which led down to the beach.

Sheltie didn't go. He was busy in his new paddock making friends with three stray ducks. Sheltie had rounded the ducks into a tight corner and stood with his head on one side listening to their noisy quacking.

Dad gave Joshua a piggyback ride as they all made their way slowly down the footpath to the beach.

At the end of the footpath there were twenty-eight wooden steps which led down on to the sand. Emma counted them all.

Once on the beach, Emma ran down towards the sea. She pulled off her shoes and socks and paddled in the foamy waves.

Further down along the beach some people were sitting on the sand: a man and a woman, and a young girl of Emma's age with dark, curly hair. When the girl saw Emma she got up and walked down to the sea.

Emma pulled a face. The girl was Alice Parker. She went to the same school as Emma. Emma didn't like Alice Parker very much. She was a show-off, and was always teasing Emma about Sheltie. Alice Parker had a pony too. Not a little Shetland pony like Sheltie, but a big brown one that shone like a conker.

Alice Parker was always saying that Sheltie had funny, stumpy legs and wasn't a proper pony at all. And she said that Emma looked stupid when she was riding him.

The two girls met at the water's edge.

'Hello, Alice,' said Emma, trying to be friendly.

Alice stuck her nose up in the air.

'Are you on holiday too?' asked Emma.

Alice didn't answer. She just turned and walked away.

Emma plodded back up the beach towards Mum, Dad and Joshua.

'Guess who's over there,' said Emma to Mum. She pointed along the beach with her finger.

'Is it someone you know?' asked Dad.

'It's Alice Parker from school,' said Emma. 'She's horrible.'

Mum looked over at Alice, who was now picking shells from the sand.

'She looks like a nice girl, Emma. Why don't you give her a chance? After all, if she's here on holiday too, it might be nice to have someone to play with.'

'Not Alice Parker,' said Emma. 'Besides, I've already tried.' She pulled a face. 'I'd much rather play with Joshua and Sheltie. Alice Parker calls Sheltie names. I'll never like her.'

'Maybe you'll change your mind in a day or two, Emma,' said Dad.

'I won't,' said Emma, feeling very

determined. She didn't like Alice Parker at school, and she wasn't going to like her on holiday. And that was that.

Chapter Four

The next day, Emma took Sheltie down to the beach. Sheltie was a tough little pony with a strong, steady walk. It was easy for him to take the winding footpath down to the sandy bay. But he couldn't manage the twenty-eight wooden steps, so everyone went the long way down.

Dad walked in front with Joshua sitting on his shoulders. Mum followed, carrying a picnic basket and towels for them all to sit on.

Emma led Sheltie by his reins. Sheltie plodded along, enjoying every minute of the sea breeze as it blew through his long shaggy mane. Overhead, the cries of the seagulls echoed in the blue sky. It was a beautiful summer's day.

Down on the sandy beach Emma climbed into Sheltie's saddle.

'Trot on, Sheltie.' Emma pressed with her heels and Sheltie trotted off across the bay, leaving a trail of little hoofprints in the soft golden sand.

At the water's edge, Sheltie stopped. He had never seen the sea before and he gazed out across the sparkling water. A crab scuttled by at his feet. Sheltie gave a loud blow and tossed his head as he pawed at the lapping waves.

Mum had laid the towels out on the sand and Joshua plonked himself down with his bucket and spade. Dad watched Emma and Sheltie trotting along in the surf.

'Don't go too far, Emma. Stay where we can see you,' called Dad.

Emma smiled back over her shoulder. 'We will,' she said. She rode Sheltie down to the end of the bay. Giant rocks sloped down from the cliffs into the sea. And there Summerland Bay came to an end.

There were little rock pools at the end of the beach. Emma dismounted to take a better look. Sheltie peered into a pool and saw his reflection in the water. Then he stuck his nose in and pulled out a long slimy string of seaweed. Sheltie gave the seaweed a good shake and Emma got sprayed with droplets of salty water.

Emma grabbed the other end of the seaweed. Sheltie held on fast and pulled. The seaweed tore apart and Emma sat down on the sand with a bump.

Sheltie pranced around with the seaweed hanging from his mouth. He did look funny – like a pony with a long green beard.

Emma laughed as she stood up and brushed the sand from her jeans. Just then, she noticed another pony and a rider coming along the beach, close to

the water's edge. It was Alice Parker.

'Oh no!' said Emma.

Alice Parker was riding a handsome white pony. Not a little Shetland pony like Sheltie, but a much bigger one.

Alice saw Emma and came trotting over. She brought the pony to a halt and gave a smug smile.

'Hello, Emma,' said Alice. 'I see

you've brought Stumpy on holiday with you.'

'His name's Sheltie,' said Emma. She was really cross. Emma found it hard to like Alice.

'This is Silver Lad,' said Alice. 'We're staying at Highcliff Farm. They have lots of ponies there. Proper ponies. It's a riding centre. I bet you wish you had a proper pony to ride, don't you, Emma?'

'No, I don't. I only like Sheltie. And anyway, he *is* a proper pony. He's a Shetland pony.'

Sheltie walked over to Silver Lad and looked up at the white pony. Their noses met and they sniffed each other and said hello.

'I'll give you a race,' said Alice,

smirking. 'Silver Lad against Stumpy.'

'I don't want to race,' frowned Emma. She climbed back up into Sheltie's saddle.

'You're scared,' said Alice. 'I bet Stumpy can't even run. His legs are too short!'

'Yes he can,' snapped Emma. 'Sheltie's really fast.'

'Come on then, scaredy-cat,' laughed Alice. 'Race you to the other end of the beach!'

Then Alice dug in her heels and Silver Lad took off at a canter along the stretch of beach.

Emma really didn't want to race. But Sheltie did.

Emma just squeezed gently with her heels and he was away in a flash.

Sheltie galloped after Silver Lad as fast as his little legs could carry him.

Emma hung on tightly to the reins as Sheltie raced along the shore. He wasn't fast enough though, and Silver Lad won the race easily.

'I told you so,' laughed Alice Parker. 'I told you that Stumpy couldn't run.'

Emma said nothing. She was upset and angry. It wasn't fair. Sheltie only had little legs. Emma turned Sheltie around and walked him back along the beach.

She leaned forward and patted Sheltie's neck.

'Never mind, boy. You're better than Silver Lad any day!'

Chapter Five

The next morning, Emma didn't want to go down to the beach. She didn't want to meet Alice Parker again.

Instead, she asked Mum if she could ride Sheltie out over the downs. There was a bridle path that led off from their holiday cottage across the heathland.

Mum said it was OK as long as Emma kept away from the cliff-top and didn't go too far. Emma promised, then she and Sheltie set off on an adventure all on their own.

Emma rode Sheltie along the bridle path. It was nice and quiet up there. Sheep were grazing peacefully all across the downs. The best thing of all though, was that there was no Alice Parker.

Emma had been riding for about ten minutes when she noticed something glinting up ahead, just off the bridle path.

What's that funny looking thing? thought Emma. It was a metal bar gleaming between the gorse bushes and the heather. Emma dismounted and walked up to it.

The shiny bar turned out to be the

handle of a silver shopping trolley. Just like the ones they have in supermarkets.

What's that doing up here in the middle of nowhere? Emma thought.

Sheltie saw it too and trotted over to investigate. There were some white things sticking out between the bars of the trolley. They were feathers. Three long white feathers. Emma pulled them free and Sheltie tried to eat them.

'I wonder what kind of bird these came from?' Emma said to Sheltie. Sheltie put his head over to one side, listening carefully.

The feathers were very long.

'It must have been a big bird,' said Emma. 'A seagull perhaps!' She looked up at the sky. Sheltie looked up too. But the feathers seemed far too long for a seagull.

'Maybe it was an ostrich,' laughed Emma. She held the feathers together at one end like a fan and climbed back into the saddle.

They continued on their way across the downs. Emma pretended that she was a lost princess riding across the desert. She waved the fan and tickled Sheltie's ears. Sheltie swished his tail and blew a loud raspberry.

Half an hour later, when Emma and Sheltie came back along the bridle path, the supermarket trolley had gone.

How strange! thought Emma. Who on earth would have pushed a trolley

all the way up to the downs and then taken it away again? Emma was puzzled by the mystery.

They continued slowly back to the holiday cottage, following the path round the curve of a hill.

Suddenly, the narrow track dipped

sharply and Sheltie stumbled. When Sheltie started to walk again he was limping.

'Oh, poor Sheltie,' said Emma. She slid out of the saddle. 'Have you hurt your leg?' Sheltie lowered his head and stood holding his front hoof up off the ground. Emma felt his leg and looked at his hoof, but she couldn't see anything. She was really worried.

'You poor thing. Can you manage the rest of the way? It's not far now.'

Sheltie hobbled forwards, limping, as Emma led with the reins. They walked very slowly. Each time Sheltie's foot touched the ground he lifted it again very quickly.

Emma led Sheltie off the hard stony track and on to the soft grass. She hoped it was nothing serious. She wanted to get Sheltie back to the cottage as quickly as possible.

'If we cut across here, it won't be so far,' said Emma. They walked away from the winding bridle path. Sheltie limped on as best as he could.

Suddenly the grass ahead sloped away down into a big dip, like a giant basin in the landscape. They stood on its rim overlooking the roof of an old tumbledown cottage.

Maybe someone there could help, thought Emma.

Chapter Six

A little path wound its way down to the front door. Dandelions grew up all over the front step. It looked as though nobody lived in the cottage after all.

Then Emma saw the supermarket trolley parked outside and her eyes grew wide.

While Emma was staring, an old woman came out of the cottage. She held a ginger cat cradled in her arms like a baby.

'Hello,' called the old woman. She was dressed in a funny old raincoat tied at the waist with string. But she had a nice friendly smile.

'Hello,' said Emma.

'Have you come to see the animals?' asked the old woman.

Emma didn't quite know what to say.

'We're staying at Cliff-top Cottage,' she said. 'We're on holiday. This is Sheltie. He's hurt his leg and he can't walk properly.'

Sheltie shook his mane and whinnied softly. He stood with his head low, looking at his hoof.

'Better bring him down and let me

have a look at him then,' said the old woman. Her voice sounded kind and caring.

Emma led Sheltie down the winding path into the little front garden. The old woman put the cat down and came over. She felt Sheltie's leg, then lifted his hoof and had a good look at it.

'He's got a stone caught under his shoe,' said the old woman. 'I'll fix that. Your little pony will soon be as good as new.'

She went into the cottage and came out holding a hoof pick. Sheltie stood very still and let the old woman lift his leg. She then carefully removed the stone from his hoof.

'There, that's better, isn't it, Sheltie?'

Sheltie could put his foot down comfortably now.

'What a nice friendly pony.' The woman gave Sheltie a hard pat.

Emma liked the old woman. Her name was Mary. She looked funny, but she was very kind.

Mary lived in the cottage by herself and cared for all kinds of sick and injured animals. People brought them to the cottage for Mary to look after. And sometimes the animals came all by themselves.

Mary asked Emma if she would like to see the animals. Emma said she would, but thought it best if she asked Mum and Dad first.

It wasn't far to Cliff-top Cottage. Luckily Sheltie's hoof was as good as new and he trotted back happily along the bridle path.

In no time at all Mum and Dad got to hear all about Mary and how she had helped Sheltie. Emma also told them about Mary's animal hospital and asked if she could go back and see all the animals. Dad said he would go with her that afternoon.

After lunch Emma plopped the saddle on to Sheltie's back and tightened the leather girth around his fat tummy. Then she slipped on the bridle and mounted.

Mum and Joshua stood outside the cottage and watched as Emma, Sheltie and Dad made their way along the bridle path and out over the heathland.

'Bye-bye,' gurgled Joshua, who was just learning to talk.

'Be back at five in time for tea, you two!' Mum called after them. Emma smiled and gave a wave. Sheltie blew a raspberry and made Dad laugh.

*

Mary came out of the cottage when she heard Emma, Sheltie and Dad approaching.

'Hello,' Dad called cheerfully when he saw Mary.

Mary greeted them with a warm smile. 'Hello, Emma. Hello, Sheltie.'

Sheltie shook his head and tossed his mane.

Dad introduced himself, then Mary took them behind the cottage to see the animal hospital and to meet all her patients.

There was Harold, a hairy goat with a gammy leg, and Doris, an old seaside donkey that nobody wanted any more. Poor Doris was blind in one eye. Harold and Doris both lived in a little field which backed on to the cottage.

A fox that had been hit by a car lay on some straw in a wire cage.

'He's still a bit poorly,' said Mary. 'But he's going to be fine.'

There was a badger too, that had hurt its foot, several rabbits, a family of hedgehogs, two seagulls and an owl.

And in a wooden pen at the far end of Mary's hospital was a beautiful white swan.

'This is Snowy,' said Mary. 'He flew into some overhead wires and damaged his wing. It's mended now but he won't be able to fly for a while. Every day I put Snowy in the supermarket trolley and take him up to Hollow's Pond on the heath. He has a little swim and then I bring him

139

back. He's ever so gentle. When he can fly and look after himself I'll release him back into the wild.'

Now Emma knew where those long white feathers came from!

Mary told Emma and Dad how all

the animals would eventually go back to their homes when they were well enough. All except Harold and Doris. They were like family to Mary.

'If you like, Emma,' said Mary, 'tomorrow you can come with me to Hollow's Pond and watch Snowy swim. Would that be all right?'

'Oh, can I please, Dad?' said Emma.

Dad said she could. He liked Mary and thought she was a nice, kind old lady.

'And can Sheltie come too?' asked Emma.

'Of course,' said Mary.

Sheltie threw back his head and let out the loudest snort Emma had ever heard. Sheltie liked Mary too.

Chapter Seven

In the morning, Mum gave Emma two small fruit pies which she had brought with her from Little Applewood. She popped them into a paper bag for Emma to take along to Mary.

Dad went with Emma and Sheltie as far as Mary's cottage, just to make sure that the visit to Hollow's Pond was still all right.

Mary was out in the back field,

hand-feeding Harold the goat and Doris the donkey with carrots and apple quarters. When they arrived, Emma rode Sheltie round to the back of the cottage and right up to the fence.

Harold stood on his hind legs with his front hoofs resting on the wooden rail and rubbed noses with Sheltie. Doris gave a low bray. It seemed to be her way of saying, 'Hello, Sheltie.'

Emma slipped out of the saddle and held Sheltie's reins. She smiled at Dad and handed Mary the fruit pies.

'What a lovely treat,' said Mary. 'I know who would like a piece of these.' Harold was doing a funny little dance and staring at the paper bag.

'You can have a piece later, you greedy goat,' laughed Mary.

She took the pies inside then went to Snowy's pen and gently lifted the swan up into her arms and put him in the trolley. Snowy seemed very tame and didn't mind Mary picking him up. Emma guessed that Snowy was looking forward to his morning swim.

Mary pushed the trolley and Dad watched Emma lead Sheltie alongside, up the narrow track which led away from the cottage.

'See you back at home,' said Dad.

Hollow's Pond wasn't very far. It was near the spot where Emma had first seen the supermarket trolley hidden in the bushes.

Mary lifted Snowy from the trolley

and carried him over a grassy hump
and down into a shallow dip on the
other side. In the hollow was a little
secret pond, hidden away from the
rest of the heath. You would never

145

have guessed that there was a pond there at all if you didn't know about it.

Long reeds grew all around the pond at the water's edge. Mary lowered Snowy to the ground and the swan waddled into the shallow water. He waggled his tail feathers and swam out to the middle of the pond.

Emma and Sheltie watched as Snowy glided gracefully across the water. He looked so beautiful. No one would ever have known that he had damaged his wing.

Sheltie grazed on the grassy bank, nibbling at a patch of dandelions, while Emma and Mary watched the swan.

After a while, Mary took some lettuce leaves from her pocket and dipped them in the water. Snowy glided over and waddled up on to the bank. He took the leaves and then shook his tail feathers. Mary picked him up and carried him back to the trolley.

'Before we go back,' said Mary, 'I'll show you another secret.'

'Another secret!' chirped Emma.

Sheltie pricked up his ears.

Mary told Emma about a pair of peregrine falcons which were nesting on a ledge on the cliff-face.

'They are very rare birds,' Mary said. 'And they're hatching two eggs. Come along, I'll show you.'

Chapter Eight

They pushed the trolley across to the cliff-top.

Emma tethered Sheltie and followed Mary to the edge of the cliff.

Mary held Emma's hand and they stood looking down the steep cliff-face.

'Be careful now, Emma,' said Mary. 'Don't stand too near.'

They peered over the edge. Below,

halfway down, a narrow path hugged the cliff-face. And beyond that, a long, long way down, was the beach. Emma could see Alice Parker down there riding Silver Lad along the shore.

Emma noticed how far down the beach was. Her legs felt wobbly. Alice Parker looked *so* tiny, like a small round pebble.

Mary pointed to a ledge. Two

falcons were perched on the rocky lip. One bird was sitting on a nest.

'The eggs should hatch soon,' said Mary. 'And we should see two fluffy chicks before the week is out.'

'Oh,' cooed Emma. 'That would be wonderful.'

Then Emma looked at the cliff path.

'Where does that lead to?' she asked.

'The cliff path runs right down to the beach,' said Mary. 'But it's very dangerous. Don't *you* ever go down there,' she added.

'I won't,' said Emma. The path looked far too dangerous. Although there were some wider bits, it was mainly very narrow.

*

Emma was back at Cliff-top Cottage in time for lunch. Dad had made some salad rolls and they all sat outside in the garden to eat them. Then they had some delicious strawberry ice-cream.

Emma was so excited. She told Mum and Dad all about Snowy and how graceful he was when he swam. And she told them about the peregrine falcons and the nest.

'You were very lucky to see a pair nesting like that,' said Dad. 'You must be careful not to disturb them.'

Emma smiled. 'Don't worry, they're too far away.' She was having such a wonderful holiday.

That afternoon, they left Sheltie in the paddock, grazing in the summer sunshine, and went for a drive to the little quay around the next bay.

Colourful fishing boats bobbed up and down in the harbour. Emma's family walked along the thin strip of beach collecting shells. Emma found a piece of driftwood in the shape of a fish. Mum said she would help Emma to paint it. Emma wanted to give the driftwood to Mary as a present when they left.

Mum said she would like to meet Mary and pay her animal hospital a visit. She wanted Joshua to see Snowy and the animals. And Dad was hoping to see the two falcons.

When they arrived back at Cliff-top Cottage Emma decided to ride Sheltie across the heathland. She said she would pop in to see Mary and ask if it would be all right to bring all the family over the following day.

Mary's cottage was only ten minutes' ride away, but when Emma and Sheltie got there Mary was nowhere to be seen. All the animals were there. Harold and Doris were in the field. The trolley was there, and so was Snowy in his little pen. But there was no sign of Mary.

Emma thought that perhaps the old lady had gone to watch the falcons. She turned Sheltie and rode over to the cliff-top. Mary wasn't there either.

Emma stood up in the stirrups and looked around. She couldn't see the old lady anywhere.

Sheltie raised his head and sniffed
at the air. Then he blew a loud snort.

Emma slid off the saddle and left
Sheltie to nibble at the grass as he

usually did. But Sheltie was more interested in the edge of the cliff-top. He trotted over to the rocky edge and gave several more noisy snorts. Then Sheltie pawed at the rock with his hoof.

What is he so upset about? thought Emma. She went over to take a look. Emma stood as near to the edge of the cliff as she dared and peered over. She gasped in horror at what she saw.

There below, on the narrow cliff path, were Alice Parker and Silver Lad!

Chapter Nine

Emma could see that Alice had taken Silver Lad up the cliff path from the beach and now they were stuck. The poor pony was terrified and had refused to go any further.

Alice stood beside Silver Lad on the narrow path, unable to move. She looked very scared.

It was a long way down to the beach and the cliff-face was very steep. Alice clung on to Silver Lad's reins and looked up at Emma, pressing herself against the cliff-wall. She was so pleased to see Emma that she burst into tears.

'Please help!' sobbed Alice. 'We're stuck. Silver Lad won't move. He won't go forward and I daren't turn him.' Alice was really very frightened. Her face was almost white.

'Just stay there and keep still,' said Emma. 'Don't move at all. I'll take Sheltie and fetch help.'

Emma thought she would ride back to Mary's cottage to see if she had come home. But then she thought she could gallop back quickly and fetch Dad. He'd know what to do.

But before Emma could do anything, Sheltie had gone to the rescue. He had seen where the cliff path began between a gap in two big rocks and was already on his way.

'Sheltie!' called Emma. 'Come back!'

But it seemed as though Sheltie knew that Alice and Silver Lad were in serious trouble. He carefully stepped on to the narrow path.

It was very steep at first, but then the path levelled out a bit and became a little wider.

Emma followed behind Sheltie. She was scared, but took the path slowly, one step at a time.

'Be careful,' cried Alice from below.

Silver Lad let out a pitiful whinny.

Sheltie was a very brave pony. And being small, with a strong steady walk, he was able to tread the path easily. Emma walked close behind, keeping her back to the cliff-wall and moving along sideways, trying not to look down.

The wind whipped her cheeks and the waves crashed on to the beach below. Emma bit her bottom lip and called to Alice.

'We're coming! Don't be scared,' Emma shouted, even though she was scared herself.

Sheltie carried on. He was very sure-footed and didn't seem to be afraid. He seemed determined to rescue Alice and Silver Lad.

As he moved forward, Emma drew
in her breath and stood watching, as
still as a statue. She could see that the
pathway just in front of Sheltie was
dangerously narrow. And one small
part was missing where the rock had
crumbled away.

Emma gasped as Sheltie nearly put his foot over the edge.

'Sheltie, please be careful,' cried Emma.

Sheltie looked round and shook his head with a loud snort as if to say, 'I'm all right, Emma.'

Chapter Ten

With only a few metres left to go, Sheltie suddenly heard a voice calling from above. He looked up. It was Mary. The old woman looked very worried as she peered down at Emma and Sheltie from the cliff-top above them.

'Take care, Emma,' called Mary. 'Don't make any sudden movements, and stay close to the cliff-face. I'm coming to get you.'

Mary began to climb down on to the path. Emma edged her way back and took Mary's outstretched hand.

From the cliff-top they could see that Sheltie had reached Alice. He stood on a wider piece of path just in front of Silver Lad and turned around.

Emma called down to Alice. 'Reach forward and take hold of Sheltie's tail!'

Alice was so frightened she could hardly move. Sheltie gave a soft snort.

Mary spoke softly to Alice. 'Move forward slowly,' she said. 'Look straight ahead. Hold on tightly to Sheltie's tail and lead the other pony.'

Alice took Silver Lad's reins, then holding on to Sheltie's tail they began to move slowly.

Seeing Sheltie seemed to give Silver Lad the courage he needed to move forward. The frightened pony trod carefully and followed Alice and Sheltie.

When Sheltie reached the narrowest part where the path had crumbled away, Emma called down gently to Sheltie. 'Go on, boy. Just a little further.'

Sheltie looked up and answered with a soft blow. He carefully stepped past the crumbling edge and led Alice on. But Silver Lad was too frightened. The pony stopped again and Alice had to let go of his rein.

Mary went down on to the path again and called Sheltie forward. She reached out for his rein and helped

him along the last bit, up on to the
cliff-top.

When they were safely away from
the path, Alice burst into tears.

'I was so scared,' she sobbed, and

threw her arms around Emma, giving her a big hug.

Before anyone had time to blink, Sheltie went back down on to the path. Silver Lad was still stuck. The poor pony was terrified and all on his own.

Sheltie stood at the start of the path and made funny pony noises. Soft snorts and whinnies that called to Silver Lad as if to say, 'Come on, you're nearly there.'

Sheltie nodded his head and Silver Lad moved slowly forward on his own. He trod with care and began walking towards Sheltie.

Mary, Emma and Alice held their breath as Sheltie and Silver Lad clambered up on to the cliff-top.

Sheltie nuzzled up to Silver Lad. The poor pony was shaking from head to hoof.

Mary stroked the pony's muzzle and spoke softly to him. Her voice soon calmed Silver Lad down.

Emma went over to Sheltie and put her arms around his neck.

'Oh, Sheltie. You were so brave.'

Sheltie gave a loud snort, then pushed his soft velvet muzzle against Emma's cheek and blew hot air down the side of her neck.

'You have a very special pony there, Emma,' said Alice.

'I know,' said Emma. 'I don't know what would have happened if it wasn't for Sheltie.'

Alice had stopped crying. 'I'm so

very sorry I've been horrible to you and Sheltie, Emma.' Her eyes were all red and puffy. She looked very embarrassed. 'I can't thank you and Sheltie enough for saving us.' Alice looked down at her shoes.

'We had better get you two back home,' said Mary.

They led the two ponies back to Mary's cottage and the old woman telephoned Highcliff Farm, where Alice was staying.

Alice's mother and father drove up with a man from the riding school to collect Alice and Silver Lad. They were both very grateful to Emma and said they would like to send her a little present as a special thank you when they got back to Little Applewood.

Emma rode back to Cliff-top Cottage on Sheltie to tell Mum and Dad all about their adventure.

'What a silly girl Alice was,' said Mum. 'Fancy taking a pony up such a dangerous path.'

Although Mum and Dad said that Emma should never have attempted to rescue Alice alone, they understood that Sheltie had taken the lead. Emma and Sheltie had been very brave. Mum and Dad were so proud of their daughter and her little pony.

'It's a good job Sheltie came along with us on holiday after all, isn't it, Mum?' said Emma.

Chapter Eleven

The rest of the holiday passed by very quickly. Emma didn't see Alice Parker on the beach again. Not even once. Apart from a few other families they had the golden sands all to themselves.

Each day Emma rode Sheltie along the shore. Sheltie was excited by the smell of the sea and the soft ground beneath his feet. He pranced about on the sand and Emma raced him along the stretch of beach, sending the seagulls screaming and soaring over their heads. It was wonderful.

Every day they also went to visit Mary and the animals.

By the following week the fox was up and walking and Mary said that in another week he would be strong enough to be released back into the wild.

The badger was getting better too. And Snowy could now spread his wings and flap them with ease. He still couldn't fly yet, but Mary said that he soon would.

Emma and Sheltie also went with Mary to Hollow's Pond and watched the swan take his daily swim.

'Just think,' said Emma, 'when I'm back home, Snowy's wing will be as good as new and he'll be flying free. Do you think he will remember us?'

'I'm sure he will,' smiled Mary. 'How could anyone forget you and Sheltie?'

Sheltie blew a raspberry and shook his mane.

They strolled to the edge of the cliff-top and watched the two falcons. The hen-bird sat on the nest and Mary said that the eggs should be hatching very soon.

On their last full day in Summerland Bay, Emma and Sheltie took Mum, Dad and Joshua to visit Mary. They saw all the animals and strolled up to the cliff-top to see the falcons.

The two chicks had finally hatched! They sat in the nest and poked their fluffy little heads out from beneath their mother's wing.

Dad looked through his binoculars as the cock-bird brought food to the nest.

'Birdy!' laughed Joshua.

'This has been the best holiday ever,' said Emma.

Before they left, Emma gave Mary the painted driftwood fish that Mum had helped her to decorate as a present. It was beautifully painted, with colourful scales, eyes and fins.

'I shall treasure it always,' said Mary with a little tear in the corner of her eye. She gave Emma a big hug.

Sheltie nuzzled Mary's cheek with his nose and gave her face a lick.

Chapter Twelve

The next morning the holiday finally came to an end.

Emma helped Mum to pack up all their things and Dad tied the cases on to the roof-rack on top of the car.

When everything was ready Emma felt very sad to leave the holiday cottage. Sheltie was settled safely in the horse trailer and they climbed into the car and set off for home.

Mary had come to the cottage to say goodbye and Emma and Joshua waved as the car pulled away and disappeared down the track to join the main road.

'I'll write to you from Little Applewood,' Emma called through the open window.

Mary smiled and waved until the car was out of sight.

At home, Emma told her best friend Sally all about her wonderful holiday. Sally had ridden over on Minnow as soon as she knew they were back. Sheltie liked Minnow and his eyes twinkled with delight when he saw him.

Emma and Sally went riding

together all over the countryside around Little Applewood. And when they rode up to Horseshoe Pond they sat and talked about Mary, Snowy the swan and all the animals in Mary's hospital.

Emma wrote to Mary, and very soon afterwards a letter arrived for Emma from Summerland Bay. Inside the envelope along with Mary's reply was a cutting from the local newspaper. 'DARING CLIFF-TOP RESCUE' was the heading on the page.

Mum read the article aloud:

'While on holiday at Summerland Bay, brave Emma Matthews and her fearless Shetland pony, Sheltie, came to the rescue of Alice Parker and her pony Silver Lad when they became trapped on the cliff path overlooking the sea. Without a thought for his own safety, brave Sheltie climbed down on to the narrow cliff path and with Emma's help led the trapped girl and her pony to safety in a daring rescue. Emma Matthews and Sheltie live in Little Applewood.'

'You and Sheltie are famous, Emma!' said Dad.

Emma blushed with pride. She was very pleased. 'But it was Sheltie really,' said Emma.

That morning a parcel had also arrived for Emma. It was from Mr and Mrs Parker. Emma ripped open the wrapping paper and inside was a lovely book all about Shetland ponies. There was also a note from Alice. It read:

Dear Emma,

I hope you like the book Mummy and Daddy have sent you. I chose it for you myself because I know you like Shetlands. There are lots of pictures and some of the ponies look just like Sheltie. I think Sheltie is the bravest pony in the world and I hope we can all become friends.

Thank you again for coming to my rescue in Summerland Bay. See you in school.

Love, Alice

'What a nice letter,' said Mum.

Outside, Sheltie was waiting in the paddock for his breakfast. He was tossing his head and making the noises he always did when he was hungry. Sheltie's eyes shone brightly beneath his long bushy mane as he saw Emma looking out from the kitchen window.

'Sheltie really is the best pony ever, isn't he?' said Emma. 'What a lovely holiday we had. And Sheltie made it extra special, didn't he? Maybe Alice Parker isn't so bad after all.'

Then she trotted happily out to the paddock to give Sheltie his breakfast.

Choosing a brilliant book
can be a tricky business...
but not any more

www.puffin.co.uk

The best selection of books at your fingertips

So get clicking!

Searching the site is easy – you'll find
what you're looking for at the click of a mouse,
from great authors to brilliant books and more!

Everyone's got different taste . . .

I like stories that make me laugh

Animal stories are definitely my favourite

I'd say fantasy is the best

I like a bit of romance

It's got to be adventure for me

I really love poetry

I like a good mystery

Whatever you're into, we've got it covered . . .

www.puffin.co.uk

Psst!
What's happening?

sneakpreviews@puffin

For all the inside information on the hottest new books,

click on the Puffin

www.puffin.co.uk

Read more in Puffin

For complete information about books available from Puffin – and Penguin – and how to order them, contact us at the appropriate address below. Please note that for copyright reasons the selection of books varies from country to country.

www.puffin.co.uk

In the United Kingdom: Please write to Dept EP, Penguin Books Ltd,
Bath Road, Harmondsworth, West Drayton, Middlesex UB7 ODA

In the United States: Please write to Penguin Putnam Inc., P.O. Box 12289,
Dept B, Newark, New Jersey 07101–5289 or call 1–800–788–6262

In Canada: Please write to Penguin Books Canada Ltd,
10 Alcorn Avenue, Suite 300, Toronto, Ontario M4V 3B2

In Australia: Please write to Penguin Books Australia Ltd,
P.O. Box 257, Ringwood, Victoria 3134

In New Zealand: Please write to Penguin Books (NZ) Ltd,
Private Bag 102902, North Shore Mail Centre, Auckland 10

In India: Please write to Penguin Books India Pvt Ltd,
11 Panscheel Shopping Centre, Panscheel Park, New Delhi 110 017

In the Netherlands: Please write to Penguin Books Netherlands bv,
Postbus 3507, NL–1001 AH Amsterdam

In Germany: Please write to Penguin Books Deutschland GmbH,
Metzlerstrasse 26, 60594 Frankfurt am Main

In Spain: Please write to Penguin Books S. A., Bravo Murillo 19,
1° B, 28015 Madrid

In Italy: Please write to Penguin Italia s.r.l.,
Via Felice Casati 20, I–20124 Milano

In France: Please write to Penguin France S. A.,
17 rue Lejeune, F–31000 Toulouse

In Japan: Please write to Penguin Books Japan, Ishikiribashi Building,
2–5–4, Suido, Bunkyo-ku, Tokyo 112

In South Africa: Please write to Longman Penguin Southern Africa (Pty) Ltd,
Private Bag X08, Bertsham 2013